GW005855953

A TREASURY

OF

CHILDREN'S

POETRY

Running Press
Philadelphia • London

Canadian representatives: General Publishing Co.,
Ltd., 30 Lesmill Road, Don Mills, Ontario M3B
2T6. International representatives: Worldwide
Media Services, Inc., 30 Montgomery Street,
Jersey City, New Jersey 07302.

Library of Congress Cataloging-in-Publication
Number 93-85533

ISBN 1-56138-362-7

This book may be ordered by mail from the
publisher. Please add $1.00 for postage and
handling. *But try your bookstore first!*

Running Press Book Publishers
125 South Twenty-second Street
Philadelphia, Pennsylvania 19103-4399

Contents

Introduction

Childhood is a giddy romp through a world of wonder. Children see the world through innocent eyes, with open minds and hearts. To a child, everything is worth looking at and asking about. "Why" is the most common childhood question—and "Because!" is the most common explanation.

In rhyme, classic and contemporary poets, from

Lewis Carroll to Shel Silverstein, from Christina Rossetti to e. e. cummings, offer their own explanations. Their poems, depicting people, animals, the forces of nature, and nonsense, capture the simple curiosity of childhood. Verses exploring flamingoes,

elephants, the wind, and the
fog, express all the silliness and
joy of life. Here is an informal
introduction to poetry for
young lovers of words and
whimsy, and a reminder to us
all to revel in the absurdity that
surrounds us.

After all, as children know,
life sometimes happens without
rhyme or reason.

and
Purr...

I am a very old pussy,

My name is Tabitha Jane;

I have had about fifty kittens,

So I think I mustn't
complain. . . .

Now I think I've a right,
being aged,

To take an old tabby's
repose;

To have a good breakfast
and dinner,

And to sit by the fire
and doze.

I don't care much for the
people

Who are living with me in
this house,

But I own that I love a
good fire,

And occasional herring
and mouse.

From *"An Old Cat's Confessions"*
C. P. Cranch (1813–1892)
American poet

Squiggly wiggly wriggly
jiggly
higgly piggly worm

watch it wiggle
watch it wriggle
see it squiggle

see it squirm

"Worm"

Mary Ann Hoberman, B. 1930
American writer

Come! supper is ready
Come! boys and girls now,
For here is fresh milk
From the good moolly cow.

Have done with your fife
And your row de dow dow,
And taste this sweet milk
From the good moolly cow.

Whoever is fretting
Must clear up his brow,

Or he'll have no milk
From the good moolly cow.

From "The Good Moolly Cow"
Eliza Lee Follen (1787–1860)
American poet

There was a Pig that
    sat alone,

Beside a ruined Pump.

By day and night he made
    his moan:

It would have stirred a
    heart of stone

To see him wring his hoofs
    and groan,

Because he could not jump.

From "The Melancholy Pig"
Lewis Carroll (1832–1898)
English writer

A snake is as round as a
hole in the ground,

And weasels are wavy
and sleek;

And no alligator could ever be
straighter

Than lizards that live in
a creek.

But a camel's all lumpy

And bumpy and humpy—

Any shape does for me.

From "The Camel's Complaint"
Charles E. Carryl (1841-1920)
American poet

The most beautiful bird I ever
  did see

Was the very well-balanced
  flamingo.

I saw it one night in a
  wonderful pond—

On the island of Santo
  Domingo.

On one leg it stood, and was
  standing quite good,

"So why do you do it?"
  I queried,

It thought, and it sighed, and
then slowly replied,

"If I kept them both up, I'd
get weary!"

"The Flamingo"
Randall Simms
19th-century American poet

Close by the basement
    door-step,

A representative toad

Has made, all the sultry
    summer,

    His quiet and cool abode;

And the way he bumps
    and bounces

    About on the area stones,

Would break every bone in
his body,

Except that he has no bones.

From "A Toad"

Elizabeth Akers Allen (18 2-1911)

American poet

*T*here's more in words than I
    can teach:

Yet listen, child!—I would
    not preach;

But only give some plain
    directions

To guide your speech and
    your affections.

Say not you *love* a roasted fowl,

But you may love a screaming
    owl,

And, if you can, the unwieldy
    toad

That crawls from his
    secure abode

Within the mossy garden wall

When evening dews begin
    to fall.

From "Loving and Liking"
Dorothy Wordsworth (1771–1855)
English poet

Mary had a little bird,

    With feathers bright and
      yellow,

Slender legs—upon my word,

    He was a pretty fellow!

Sweetest notes he always sung,

    Which much delighted
      Mary;

Often where his cage
      was hung,

    She sat to hear Canary.

Crumbs of bread and
    dainty seeds

  She carried to him daily,

Seeking for the early weeds,

  She decked his palace gaily.

This, my little readers, learn,

  And ever practice duly;

Songs and smiles of love return

  To friends who love you
    truly.

"The Canary"

Elizabeth Turner (1775?–1846)
English poet

One of the Clock, and
   silence deep

Then up the Stairway, black
   and steep

The old House-Cat comes
   creepy-creep

With soft feet goes from room
   to room

Her green eyes shining through
   the gloom,

   And finds all fast asleep.

"One O'Clock"
Katherine Pyle (1883–1938)
American writer

One biting winter morning,

A dusky spider swung

From off the mantle, by
his thread,

And o'er the stove-pipe
hung.

Escaped from some dim
cranny cold,

To warmer quarters there,

He seemed, upon that
slender hold,

An atom hung on air.

From "The Spider"
Hannah F. Gould (1789–1865)
American poet

With its trunk, and its tusks,
    and its big grey ears,

It's a beautiful creature,
    the elephant.

And it never forgets.
    It always remembers—

But only what it finds relevant.

"The Elevant"
Randall Simms
19th-century American poet

Come take up your hats,
    and away let us haste,

To the Butterfly's Ball,
    and the Grasshopper's
    Feast.

The trumpeter Gadfly
    has summoned the crew,

And the revels are now
    only waiting for you.

On the smooth-shaven grass
    by the side of a wood,

Beneath a broad oak
    which for ages has stood,

See the children of earth
and the tenants of air,

For an evening's amusement
together repair.

From "The Butterfly's Ball"
William Roscoe (1753–1831)
English poet

The panther is like a leopard,

Except it hasn't been
 peppered.

Should you behold a panther
 crouch,

Prepare to say Ouch.

Better yet, if called by
 a panther,

Don't anther.

"The Panther"
Ogden Nash (1902–1971)
American poet

Draw a crazy picture.

Write a nutty poem.

Sing a mumble-gumble song,

Whistle through your comb.

Do a loony-goony dance

'Cross the kitchen floor,

Put something silly in
the world

That ain't been there before.

"Put Something In"
Shel Silverstein, B. 1932
American writer

They went to sea in a sieve,
  they did;

  In a sieve they went to sea;

In spite of all their friends
  could say,

On a winter's morn, on a
  stormy day,

  In a sieve they went to sea.

And when the sieve turned
  round and round,

And everyone cried, "You'll be
  drowned!"

They called aloud, "Our sieve
  ain't big,

But we don't care a button; we
don't care a fig—

In a sieve we'll go to sea!"

Far and few, far and few,

Are the lands where
the Jumblies live.

Their heads are green,
and their hands
are blue;

And they went to sea
in a sieve.

From "The Jumblies"
Edward Lear (1812-1888)
English writer and painter

I left my head
somewhere
today.
Put it down for
just
a minute.
Under the table?
On a chair?

Wish I were

able

to say

where.

Everything I need

is

in it!

"I Left My Head"
Lilian Moore, B. 1909
American writer

*I*f ever there lived a
    Yankee lad,

Wise or otherwise, good
    or bad,

Who, seeing the birds fly,
    didn't jump

With flapping arms from stake
    or stump,

  Or, spreading the tail

  Of his coat for a sail,

Take a soaring leap from post
    or rail,

  And wonder why

  He couldn't fly,

And flap and flutter and wish
    and try—

If ever you knew a
    country dunce

Who didn't try that as often
    as once,

All I can say is, that's a sign

He never would do for a hero
of mine.

*From "Darius Green and
His Flying Machine"*

John Townsend Trowbridge
(1827–1916)
American poet

Do skyscrapers ever
grow tired

Of holding themselves
up high?

Do they ever shiver on
frosty nights

With their tops against
the sky?

Do they feel lonely sometimes

Because they have grown
so tall?

Do they ever wish they could
lie right down

And never get up at all?

"Skyscrapers"
Rachel Field (1894–1942)
American writer

My little dears, who learn to
read, pray early learn
to shun

That very silly thing indeed
which people call a pun.

Read Entick's rules, and 'twill
be found how simple
an offense

It is, to make the selfsame
sound afford a
double sense.

For instance, *ale* may make
    you *ail*, your *aunt* an *ant*
    may kill,

You in a *vale* may buy a *veil*,
    and *Bill* may pay the *bill*.

Or if to France your *bark* you
    steer, at Dover, it may be,

A *peer* appears upon the *pier*,
    who, blind, still goes
    to *sea* . . . .

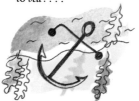

Then now you see, my little
dears, the way to make
a pun,

A trick which you, through
coming years, should
sedulously shun.

The fault admits of no defence;
for whereso'er 'tis found,

You sacrifice for *sound* the
sense; the sense is
never *sound*.

From "Cautionary Verses to
Youth of Both Sexes"
Theodore Hook (1788–1841)
English writer

A little buoy said, "Mother,
    deer,

May I go out too play?

The son is bright, the heir is
    clear,

Owe, mother, don't sey
    neigh!"

"Go fourth, my sun," the
    mother said,

The ant said, "Take
    ewer slay,

Your gneiss knew sled, awl
painted read,

Butt dew knot lose
your weigh."

From "A Misspelled Tail"
Elizabeth T. Corbett
19th-century American poet

Ladies and gentlemen,

Hobos and tramps,

Cross-eyed mosquitoes,

And bow-legged ants—

I come before you to stand
    behind you

To tell you a story

I know nothing about.

Late Thursday night, early
    Friday morning

An empty truck full of bricks

Pulled into my front yard,

Killing my cat in the
back yard.

That same night, two boys got
up to fight.

Back to back they faced
each other.

A deaf policeman heard
the noise,

Came and shot the two
dead boys.

If you don't believe this lie
    is true,

Ask the blind man—

He saw it, too.

"An Announcement"
Anonymous 20th-century poem

I'm King of the cabbages
green;

I'm King of the cabbages
red;

I'm a purple cabbage of
royal mien,

With a sensible level head.

My subjects I hold most dear,

They respect my power
and might,

And unto all persons that
venture near

We're considerate and polite.

Chorus:

We're a lot of cabbages,
    one and all;

    We're very polite, and that's

The reason why, to great
    and small,

We ever remove our hats—

Our hats, our hats, our hats,
our hats—

We ever remove our hats.

From "Old King Cabbage"
R. K. Munkittrick (1853–1911)
American poet

Somebody being a nobody,

Thinking to look like
a somebody,

Said that he thought me
a nobody:

Good little somebody-nobody,

Had you not known me
a somebody,

Would you have called me
a nobody?

"Somebody Being a Nobody"
Alfred, Lord Tennyson (1809–1892)
English poet

One day the letters went
　　to school,

And tried to learn each
　　other;

They got so mixed 'twas
　　really hard

To pick out one from t'other.

A went in first, and Z went
　　last;

The rest were all between
　　them,—

K, L, and M, and N, O, P,—

I wish you could have
seen them!

From "*The Letters at School*"
Mary Mapes Dodge (1831–1905)
American poet

One, who is not, we see; but
one, whom we see not, is.

Surely this is not that; but that
is assuredly this.

What, and wherefore, and
whence? for under is over
and under;

If thunder could be without
lightning, lightning could
be without thunder.

From "The Higher Pantheism in a Nutshell"
Algernon Charles Swinburne
(1837–1909)
English poet

The Pobble who has no toes

Had once as many as we;

When they said, "Some day
you may lose them all"—

He replied, "Fish, fiddle
de-dee!"

And his Aunt Jobiska made
him drink,

Lavender water tinged
with pink,

For she said, "The World in
general knows

There's nothing so good for a
Pobble's toes!"

From "The Pobble Who Has No Toes"
Edward Lear (1812–1888)
English painter and writer

If the butterfly courted the bee,

And the owl the porcupine;

If churches were built in
the sea,

And three times one was
nine;

If the pony rode his master,

  If the buttercups ate
    the cows,

If the cat had the dire disaster

  To be worried, sir, by
    the mouse;

If mamma, sir, sold the baby

  To a gipsy for half-a-crown;

If a gentleman, sir was a
    lady—

  The world would be
    Upside-Down!

If any or all of these wonders

Should ever come about,

I should not consider them
blunders,

For I should be Inside-Out!

"Topsyturvy World"

William Brighty Rands (1823–1882)
English poet

Into the sunshine
   Full of the light,
Leaping and flashing
   From morn till night!

Into the moonlight,
   Whiter than snow,
Waving so flower-like
   When the winds blow!

From "The Fountain"
James Russell Lowell (1819–1891)
American poet

*W*ho has seen the wind?

 Neither I nor you:

But when the leaves hang
  trembling

 The wind is passing thro'.

Who has seen the wind?

Neither you nor I:

But when the trees bow down
their heads

The wind is passing by.

"Who Has Seen the Wind?"
Christina Rossetti (1830–1894)
English poet

In Just-
spring   when the world is mud-
luscious the little
lame balloonman

whistles   far   and wee

and eddieandbill come
running from marbles and
piracies and it's
spring

when the world is puddle-
wonderful

From "in Just-"
e. e. cummings (1894–1962)
American poet

Oh, where do you come from,

   You little drops of rain,

Pitter patter, pitter patter,

   Down the window pane?

They won't let me walk,

   And they won't let me play,

And they won't let me go

   Out of doors at all today.

From "Little Raindrops"
**Aunt Effie [Jane Euphemia
Browne]** (1811–1898)
English poet

Let the rain kiss you.

Let the rain beat upon your
head with silver liquid
drops.

Let the rain sing you
a little lullaby.

The rain makes still pools
on the sidewalk.

The rain makes running pools
in the gutter.

The rain plays a little sleep-
　　song on our roof at
　　night—

And I love the rain.

"April Rain Song"
Langston Hughes (1902–1967)
American poet

By the shores of
    Gitchee Gumee

By the shining Big-Sea-Water,

Stood the wigwam of Nokomis

Daughter of the Moon,
    Nokomis.

Dark behind it rose the forest,

Rose the black and gloomy
  pine trees,

Rose the firs with cones
  upon them;

Bright before it beat the water,

Beat the clear and
  sunny water,

Beat the shining
  Big-Sea-Water.

From "The Song of Hiawatha"
Henry Wadsworth Longfellow
(1807–1882)
American poet

The Oak is called the
    king of trees,

The Aspen quivers in the
    breeze,

The Poplar grows up straight
    and tall,

The Peach tree spreads along
    the wall,

The Sycamore gives pleasant
    shade,

The Willow droops in watery
    glade,

The Fir tree useful timber
gives,

The Beech amid the forest
lives.

"Trees"

Sara Coleridge (1802–1852)
English poet

The grass so little has to do,—
A sphere of simple green,
With only butterflies to brood,
And bees to entertain....

From "The Grass"
Emily Dickinson (1830–1886)
American poet

*H*ear the sledges with
　the bells—

Silver bells!

What a world of merriment
　their melody foretells!

How they tinkle, tinkle,
　tinkle,

In the icy air of night!

While the stars that
   oversprinkle

All the heavens seem
   to twinkle

   With a crystalline delight;

Keeping time, time, time,

In a sort of Runic rhyme,

To the tintinnabulation
   that so musically wells

From the bells, bells,
   bells, bells,

Bells, bells, bells—

From the jingling and
the tinkling of the bells.

From "The Bells"
Edgar Allan Poe (1809–1849)
American writer

The fog comes
On little cat feet.

It sits looking
over harbor and city
on silent haunches
and then, moves on.

"Fog"
Carl Sandburg (1878-1967)
American poet

Between the dark and
  daylight,

  When the night is beginning
    to lower,

Comes a pause in the day's
    occupations,

  That is known as the
    Children's Hour.

I hear in the chamber
    above me

The patter of little feet,

The sound of a door that
is opened,

And voices soft and sweet.

From "The Children's Hour"
Henry Wadsworth Longfellow
(1807–1882)
American poet

*T*he sun descending in
    the west,

The evening star does shine;

The birds are silent
    in their nest,

And I must seek for mine.

The moon, like a flower

In heaven's high bower,

With silent delight

Sits and smiles on the night.

From "Night"

William Blake (1757–1827)

English poet

All that I know
  Of a certain star
Is, it can throw
  (Like an angled spar)
Now a dart of red,
  Now a dart of blue;
Till my friends have said
  They would fain see, too,
My star that dartles
    the red and the blue!

"*My Star*"

Robert Browning (1812–1889)
English poet

Me,
myself,

and I

As long as I live
I shall always be
My Self—and no other,
Just me.

From "Me"
Walter de la Mare (1873–1956)
English poet

I have a little shadow
    that goes in and out
    with me,

And what can be the use
    of him is more than
    I can see.

He is very, very like me
    from the heels up to
    the head;

And I see him jump before me,
    when I jump into my bed.

The funniest thing about him

is the way he likes
to grow—

Not at all like proper children,
which is always very
slow;

For he sometimes shoots
up taller like an
India-rubber ball,

And he sometimes gets so little
that there's none of him
at all.

From "My Shadow"
Robert Louis Stevenson (1850–1894)
Scottish writer

*W*here did you come from,
  baby dear?

Out of the everywhere
  into here.

Where did you get your eyes
  so blue?

Out of the sky as I came
  through.

*From "Where Did You
Come From, Baby Dear?"*
George MacDonald (1824–1905)
English poet

I would like to be a boat,
  And live upon the sea;
So merrily I'd float,
  With nought to trouble
    me—
      Trouble me.

But should a storm come near,

And fill me with alarms,

I would row to mother, dear—

My boat should be
her arms—

Mother's arms.

From "The Boat"
Caroline Gilman (1794-1888)
American poet

I wish I had wings,
So I could fly,
Wherever, whenever,
However high.

Over the schoolyard
Over the pond,
I'd fly to the clouds,
And way beyond!

Birds might well wonder
Who I could be,
Kicking and spinning,
And shouting out, "Wheee!"

I'd float on the air
And wave to the ground;
I'd jump off a swing,
And zoom up, uP, UP—
Not
            down.

I'd soar with the wind
As far as it goes,
And tickle the treetops
With my bare toes.

"If I Could Fly"
Louise Betts Egan
20th-century American writer

There's a little old house
   in Somewhere—

*Some*where, *Some*where,

A queer little house,
   with a Cat and
   a Mouse—

Just room enough for three.

A kitchen, a larder,

A bin for bread,

A string of candles,

Or stars instead,

A table, a chair,

And a four-post bed—

There's room for us all
in Somewhere,

For the Cat and the Mouse
and Me.

From "Somewhere"
Walter de la Mare (1873–1956)
English poet

The gingham dog and the
   calico cat

Side by side on the table sat;

'Twas half-past twelve,
   and (what do you think!)

Nor one nor t'other
   had slept a wink!

  The old Dutch clock
    and the Chinese plate

  Appeared to know
    as sure as fate

There was going to be
   a terrible spat.

(I wasn't there; I simply state

What was told to me
by the Chinese plate!)

From "The Duel"
Eugene Field (1850–1895)
American poet

Who would be
A mermaid fair,
Singing alone,
Combing her hair
Under the sea,
In a golden curl
With a comb of pearl,
On a throne?

From "The Mermaid"
Alfred, Lord Tennyson (1809–1892)
English poet

There was a naughty boy,
   A naughty boy was he,
He ran away to Scotland
   The people for to see—
      There he found
      That the ground
      Was as hard
      That a yard
      Was as long,
      That a song
      Was as merry,

That a cherry
Was as red—
That lead
Was as weighty
That fourscore
Was as eighty
That a door
Was as wooden
As in England—
So he stood in his shoes
And he wondered,

He wondered,
He stood in his shoes
And he wondered.

From "There Was a Naughty Boy"
John Keats (1785–1821)
English poet

Wynken, Blynken, and Nod
   one night

Sailed off in a
   wooden shoe—

Sailed on a river of
   crystal light,

Into a sea of dew.

"Where are you going, and
   what do you wish?"

The old moon asked
   the three.

"We have come to fish for
   the herring fish

That live in this
   beautiful sea;

Nets of silver and gold
   have we!"

   Said Wynken,

   Blynken,

   And Nod.

From "Wynken, Blynken, and Nod"
Eugene Field (1850-1895)
American poet

These little Songs,
Found here and there,
Floating in air
By forest and lea,
Or hillside heather,
In houses and throngs,

Or down by the sea—
Have come together,
How, I can't tell.
But I know full well
No witty goose-wing
On an inkstand begot   'em;
Remember each place
And moment of grace,
In summer or spring,
Winter or autumn,

By sun, moon, stars,
Or a coal in the bards,
In market or church,
Graveyard or dance,
When they came without
  search,
Were found as by chance.
A word, a line,
You may say are mine;
But the best in these songs,

Whatever it be,

To you, and to me,

And to no one belongs.

"These Little Songs"
William Allingham (1824–1889)
Irish poet

From breakfast on through all
   the day

At home among my friends
   I stay,

But every night I go abroad

Afar into the Land of Nod.

All by myself I have to go,

With none to tell me what
   to do—

All alone beside the streams

And up the mountain-sides
of dreams.

From "The Land of Nod"
Robert Louis Stevenson (1850–1894)
Scottish writer

In jumping and tumbling
  We spend the whole day,
Till night by arriving
  Has finished our play.

What then? One and all,
  There's no more to be said,
As we tumbled all day,
  So we tumble to bed.

"Tumbling"
Anonymous 18th-century poem

This book has been bound using handcraft methods, and Smyth-sewn to ensure durability.

The dust jacket was designed by E. June Roberts.

The interior was designed by Christian Benton.

The illustrations are by Allan Drummond.

The text was compiled by David Borgenicht and edited by Melissa Stein.

The text was set in CG Collage by Deborah Lugar.

Acknowledgments

P. 16: Copyright © 1973 by Mary Ann Hoberman, reprinted by permission of Gina Macoby Literary Agency; p. 38: From *Verses from 1929 On* by Ogden Nash, copyright © 1940 by Ogden Nash, reprinted by permission of Little, Brown and Company, also copyright © 1959 by Ogden Nash, reprinted by permission of Curtis Brown, Ltd.; p. 42: From *A Light in the Attic* by Shel Silverstein, copyright © 1981 by Evil Eye Music, Inc., reprinted by permission of HarperCollins Publishers and Edite Kroll Literary Agency; pp. 46–47: From *See My Lovely Poison Ivy* by Lilian Moore, copyright © 1975 by Lilian Moore, reprinted by permission of Marian Reiner for the author;